RISING STARS
Maths

Fluency with Fractions

TEACHER'S GUIDE

Steph King

YEAR 1

Rising Stars UK Ltd
7 Hatchers Mews, Bermondsey Street, London, SE1 3GS

www.risingstars-uk.com

Every effort has been made to trace copyright holders and obtain their permission for the use of copyright materials. The authors and publisher will gladly receive information enabling them to rectify any error or omission in subsequent editions. All facts are correct at time of going to press.

Published 2014
Reprinted 2014, 2015
Text, design and layout © Rising Stars UK Ltd.

The right of Steph King to be identified as the author of this work has been asserted by her in accordance with the Copyright, Design and Patents Act 1998.

Author: Steph King
Consultant: Cherri Moseley
Publisher: Fiona Lazenby
Project Manager: Debbie Allen
Editorial: Katharine Timberlake, Kate Manson
Cover design: Burville-Riley Partnership
Design: Marc Burville-Riley
Typesetting: Fakenham Prepress Solutions
Illustrations: Louise Forshaw / Advocate Art, Richard and Benjamin,
    Fakenham Prepress Solutions
CD-ROM development: Alex Morris

British Library Cataloguing in Publication Data.
A CIP record for this book is available from the British Library.

ISBN: 978-1-78339-180-6

Printed by: Ashford Colour Press Ltd, Gosport, Hants

Contents

Fractions in the 2014 National Curriculum

The National Curriculum aims to ensure that all pupils become fluent in the fundamentals of mathematics, can reason mathematically and can solve problems by applying their mathematics. With a significant shift in expectations in the 2014 Programme of Study, children are required to work with and calculate using a range of fractions at an earlier stage. Achieving fluency will depend on developing conceptual understanding through a variety of practical and contextual opportunities.

Statutory requirements and non-statutory guidance

At first glance, the statutory requirements for the Fractions domain for younger children may not appear to be that extensive. However, it is important to note that each 'objective' is made up of a range of different skills and knowledge that need to be addressed. We must remember that mastery of one aspect does not necessarily imply mastery of another.

The Programme of Study also provides non-statutory guidance that helps to clarify, secure and extend learning in each domain to best prepare children for the next stage of mathematical development. Units in this *Fluency with Fractions* series, therefore, also address some aspects of the non-statutory guidance. These objectives are flagged where applicable.

Fractions across the domains

Learning about fractions is not exclusive to the Fractions domain in the Programme of Study. Conceptual understanding of fractions is also addressed and applied through work on time, turns, angles and through many other aspects of measurement, geometry and also statistics. We must also remember to continue to practise and extend learning from previous year groups even if a concept is not explicitly covered in the Programme of Study for the current year group. The other domains provide useful opportunities for this.

Making the links: decimals, percentages, ratio and proportion

Children will first experience decimals in the context of measurement. However, security with place value is vital if they are to truly understand how the position of a digit on either side of the decimal point determines its size. Place value charts and grids are used in this series of books to continue to reinforce this concept and to help children make sense of tenths, hundredths and thousandths.

As children progress through the Programmes of Study, they will later meet percentages. Recognising that a fraction such as $\frac{25}{100}$ can be written as $25 \div 100$, and therefore as 0.25, will help make the connection to 25%.

Finding and identifying equivalent fractions will later pave the way for understanding equivalent ratios.

For this reason, within the *Fluency with Fractions* series, the Year 4 book includes work on decimals, Year 5 includes percentages and Year 6 goes on to incorporate ratio and proportion.

Developing conceptual understanding through the use of resources

Children should be given opportunities to develop conceptual understanding through a range of practical experiences and the use of visual representations to help them make sense of fractions. Manipulatives, such as Base 10 apparatus, cubes and counters, along with other resources, should be used skilfully to model concepts and provide a reference point to help children make connections for future learning. Moving in this way from concrete resources to pictorial representations to symbolic notation for fractions will help to secure conceptual understanding.

Developing mathematical language

Language is often cited as a barrier to learning, so it is important to model technical vocabulary that helps children to use it confidently and to help them explain their mathematical thinking and reasoning. Appropriate language structures are suggested throughout the Units.

Using representations to support understanding

Fractions is a part of mathematics that children often find more difficult to learn than other areas. This, in turn, is often the result of teachers finding the concepts more difficult to teach. We need to help children to see what we mean and make links to other familiar representations that they know, e.g. number lines.

Historically, images to support the teaching of fractions have tended to be related to real-life examples that children see 'cut-up' and shared. Pizzas, cakes and chocolate are examples of this. Although these representations are valuable (particularly circular images that will later inform work on pie charts), it is the linear image that directly relates to the number line that will support the transition of concrete to abstract when counting and calculating.

Throughout the *Fluency with Fractions* resources, fraction bar images are used in each year level to introduce the concept of fractions as equal parts of a whole, equivalence, counting (linked to the number line) and calculating.

The following diagrams provide a few generic examples to illustrate how different images are used. Templates for some useful images are provided on the accompanying CD-ROM.

• Fractions as equal parts of one whole.

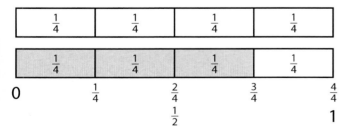

• Linking fractions to counting on a number line to reinforce that fractions are numbers in their own right. Counting paves the way for calculating.

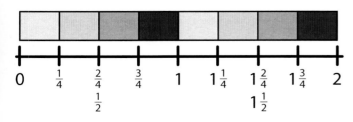

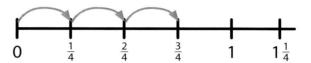

• Developing a range of images to explore equivalent fractions.

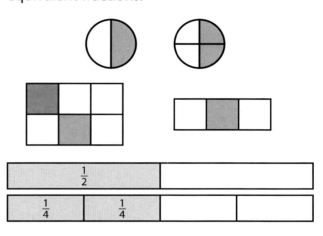

• Comparing fractions on a number line.

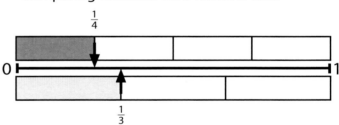

• Using fraction bars to support early calculation of fractions of amounts.

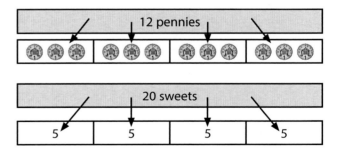

• Using fraction bars to support identifying an amount represented by a fraction.

12			

3

3	3	3	3

How to use this book

The Units in this book support the development of conceptual understanding of fractions and are intended to be used to introduce concepts. Learning should be practised and revisited regularly using other resources to consolidate and deepen understanding.

Each Unit within the books is structured in the same way, providing guidance to support teachers and an example teaching sequence.

Tasks can be used as suggested or adapted accordingly to meet the needs of each setting. Guided learning provides an opportunity for the adult to take learning forward with a group or to take part in an activity that has a greater problem-solving element and where language may be more demanding. Additional editable resource sheets are provided on the accompanying CD-ROM to support this.

Bold text shows the link to the NC objectives or the non-statutory guidance.

Please check that prior learning is in place before working on this unit.

This section helps teachers to make connections through the use of visual representations and language structures.

Each Unit includes a Talking point page that can be displayed on the interactive whiteboard or photocopied to give to children. The visual images and prompt questions help to contextualise the concept of fractions for children.

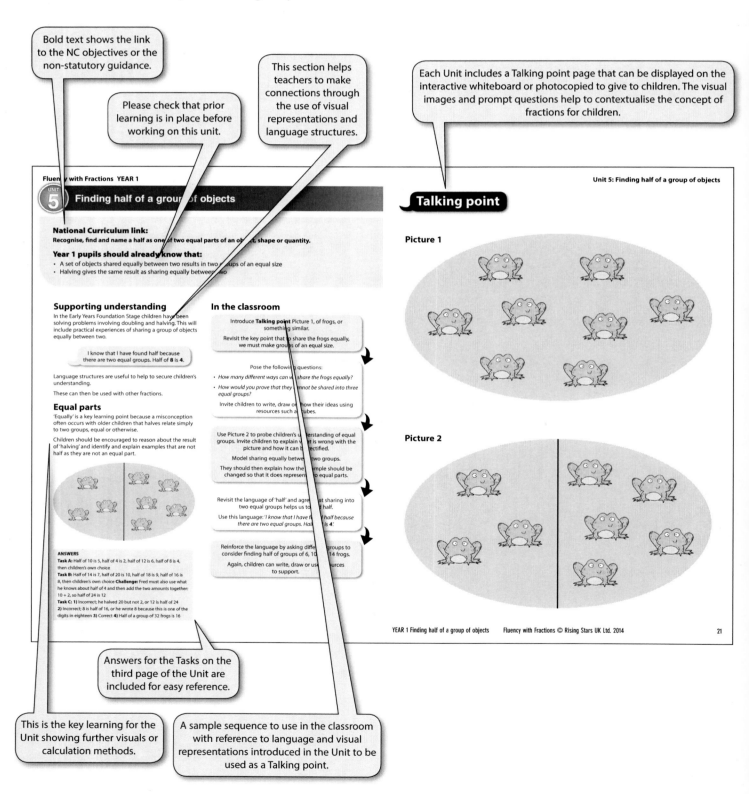

Answers for the Tasks on the third page of the Unit are included for easy reference.

This is the key learning for the Unit showing further visuals or calculation methods.

A sample sequence to use in the classroom with reference to language and visual representations introduced in the Unit to be used as a Talking point.

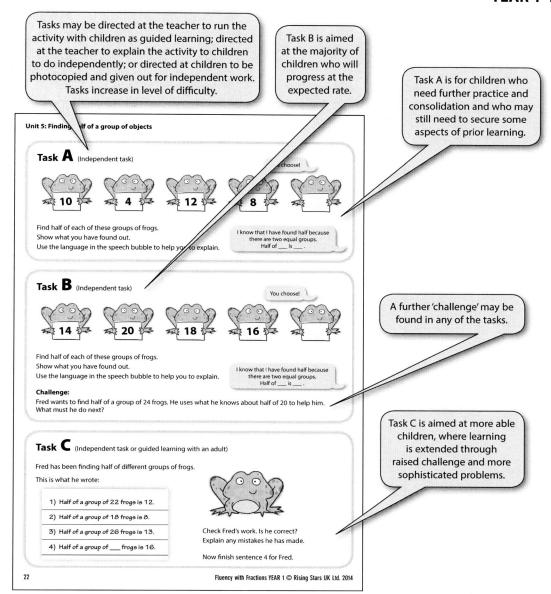

Curriculum mapping grid

The grid below shows in which Units objectives from the 2014 National Curriculum Programme of Study for Year 1 are covered. Note that objectives are revisited regularly and learning progressed in subsequent units. In the National Curriculum link section of each Unit, bold text is used to indicate which specific part of the overarching objective is addressed within the Unit, since objectives often cover a range of different knowledge and skills (particularly for younger age groups).

	Unit														
	1	2	3	4	5	6	7	8	9	10	11	12	13	14	15
Connect halves and quarters to the equal sharing and grouping of sets of objects and to measures.	✔	✔		✔					✔						
Recognise, find and name a half as one of two equal parts of an object, shape or quantity.			✔	✔	✔	✔	✔				✔				✔
Recognise and combine halves and quarters as parts of a whole.								✔						✔	
Recognise, find and name a quarter as one of four equal parts of an object, shape or quantity.											✔	✔	✔	✔	✔	✔

Equal sharing all around us

National Curriculum link:

[Non-statutory guidance] **Connect halves** and quarters **to the equal sharing** and grouping **of sets of objects** and to measures.

Year 1 pupils should already know that:

- A set of objects shared equally between two results in two groups of an equal size
- Halving gives the same result as sharing equally between two

Supporting understanding

Mathematics is all around us. In the Early Years, children will have experienced number and other aspects of mathematics in focused activities and through play both inside and outside the classroom.

There are plenty of opportunities to explore fractions and 'equal sharing' in the environment and everyday life.

Language structures will also be developed to help children to talk mathematically.

> I know … is shared equally because …

> I know … is not shared equally because …

Describing equal sharing

Find and share pictures that show an object or a group of objects shared equally, e.g:

Encourage children to discuss what they notice.

This may well include the phrases 'shared', 'same', 'has the same as', 'fair', 'half', etc.

This unit focuses on 'equal sharing'.

In the classroom

Share the pictures from the **Talking point** (with the exception of the glasses and water). Ask children to discuss what they notice about each picture.

What is the same in each? Why?

Introduce other language that will help children to talk about the pictures.

How can you use the word 'share' to describe a picture?

How can you use the words 'share' and 'equal' to describe a picture?

How can the milkman share the bottles so the two houses get an equal number?

Look at one of the pictures, e.g. the pie.

Establish that we know that the pie has been shared equally because it has been cut or divided into two equal pieces.

Finally, look at the picture of the glasses and water.

What is different about this picture?

Use this language: *'I know … is not shared equally because … .'*

Pose the following questions:

- *What would we need to do so that the water is shared equally?*

- *What word can we used to describe how much of the full glass is now in each?* (Half.)

ANSWERS
Task A: Children discuss pictures **Task B:** Children's own sorting
Task C: Children's own recording, e.g. a picture of three apples on one plate and one on the other is shown shared equally as two apples on each plate

Talking point

Look at the pictures.

What is the same in each? Why?

Task **A** (Guided learning with an adult)

Use a set of pictures (some examples are given below) for children to discuss and describe in the same way as before.

Ask questions such as:
- *How can you use the word 'share' to describe a picture?*
- *How can you use the words 'share' and 'equal' to describe a picture?*

Encourage children to use the language in the speech bubble to prove what they have found out.

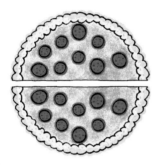  

I know ___ is / are shared equally because ___ .

Task **B** (Independent task)

Children work independently to sort a range of pictures into two sets:

Shared equally   Not shared equally

I know ___ is shared equally because ___ .

I know ___ is not shared equally because ___ .

They use the language in the speech bubbles to prove the decisions they have made.

Children can also choose a picture from each set and complete a speech bubble to describe it.

Task **C** (Independent task)

Ask children to sort a range of pictures into two sets showing those that are shared equally and those that are not.

Ask children to decide how they will label their sets.

Ask children to decide how each of the pictures that shows a set which is not shared equally should be changed so that it shows equal sharing.

Findings to be recorded in children's own way.

I know ___ is shared equally because ___ .

I know ___ is not shared equally because ___ .

UNIT 2 Equal sharing between two

National Curriculum link:

[Non-statutory guidance] **Connect halves** and quarters **to the equal sharing and grouping of sets of objects** and to measures.

Year 1 pupils should already know that:

- A set of objects shared equally between two results in two groups of an equal size
- Halving gives the same result as sharing equally between two

Supporting understanding

The main principle that builds the foundation for understanding fractions is that of sharing equally.

In Unit 1, children described a range of pictures that showed equal or unequal sharing.

Continue to use activities, pictures and apparatus to encourage children to recognise and talk about equal sharing, using language to support.

> I know … is shared equally because …

> I know … is not shared equally because …

In this unit we will explore sharing equally between two.

Equal sharing

'They solve problems, including doubling, halving and sharing' is part of the Early Learning Goal for Number.

Early experience of sharing is likely to be through the idea of 'one for you and one for me'. This supports understanding of halving and then dividing into two.

Questions to ask could include: '*Is it easier for Ali and Emma to share the teddies or the dogs equally between them? Why?*'

ANSWERS
Task A: 1) 2 **2)** 4 **3)** 3 **4)** 6 **5)** 5 **6)** Children choose a number of beads of their own to share
Task B: 1) Children's own workings to share more than 10 marbles
2) E.g. 'They have seven each and one left over' or '15 is an odd number'.
Task C: 1) Children's own workings recognising that they share an even number of marbles that is greater than 15 **2)** E.g. 18 marbles and 9 counters, 22 marbles and 11 counters.

In the classroom

Use the **Talking point** to introduce the problem:

Ali and Emma empty out their toy box.

They want to share each set of toys equally between them.

Ask children to discuss and give an example of when they have shared things equally.

Establish the key point that when a group of objects is 'shared equally' between two it results in two groups of equal size.

Emma and Ali decide to start with the teddies and dogs.

Using the pictures provided, pose the following questions for different groups:

- *How many teddies will each child have? How do you know?*

- *Why is it easier to share the teddies than the dogs?*

- *How many more dogs do they need so they can share them equally? Do you think there could be more than one answer?*

(Look for children who recognise that three more, five more, etc. would also work.)

Establish that when the teddies are shared equally between two, each child gets half the number of teddies.

They now decide to share the trucks and blocks.

Ask similar questions to those above and then start to look at the numbers that were easily shared equally and those that were not.

What do you notice about these numbers?

Where have you seen these patterns before?

Use resources, e.g. cubes, to represent odd and even numbers and model that the even numbers can be shared easily between two, whereas the odd will always have one left over.

Later on, in Key Stage 2, the one left over will be halved, e.g. 13 shared between two is $6\frac{1}{2}$.

You may find that some children already know this.

Talking point

Can you share each set of toys equally between two?

Task **A** (Independent task)

Ali and Emma also have a jar of beads in their toy box.
They take out a handful at a time and share them.

How many do they get each?

1)   2)   3)   4)   5)

6) Choose a number of beads of your own to share.

Task **B** (Independent task)

Ali and Emma also have a jar of marbles in their toy box.
There are more than 10 marbles in the jar.
They can share them equally.

1) Investigate to find the different numbers of marbles they can have.
Find a way to show what you have found out.
2) Can you prove why there are not 15 marbles in the jar?

Task **C** (Guided learning with an adult)

Ali and Emma also have a jar of marbles and a jar of counters in their toy box.
There are more than 15 marbles in the jar.
There are more marbles than counters.
They can share the marbles equally but not the counters.

1) Investigate to find the different numbers of marbles they can have.
Find a way to show what you have found out.
2) Ali and Emma share the marbles.

Hey, Ali, the number of marbles we each
have is the same as the total number of
counters in our jar!

Find two different ways to make this true.

UNIT 3   Finding half of a shape

National Curriculum link:

Recognise, find and name a half as one of two equal parts of an object, **shape** or quantity.

Year 1 pupils should already know that:

* A set of objects shared equally results in groups of an equal size
* Halving gives the same result as sharing equally between two
* When odd numbers are shared between two, there is one left over

Supporting understanding

Children have been exploring equal sharing and have identified the numbers that can be shared easily, i.e. even numbers. They recognise that when odd numbers are shared between two, there is one left over.

This unit develops the idea of equal sharing as halving, but rather than a group of objects, it focuses on just one – in this case a shape. This will later support children to deal with that 'one left over' when halving odd numbers.

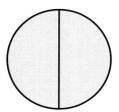 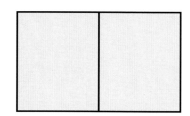

Finding halves

Find and share pictures that show an object or a group of objects shared equally, e.g:

Encourage children to discuss what they notice.

This may well include the phrases 'shared', 'split in two', 'cut down the middle', 'cut in two', etc.

Make sure to establish the 'equal sharing' and the 'equal parts' that result.

ANSWERS

Task A: Children's sorting of shapes

Task B: Children's own designs

Task C: With straight lines, there are only three different ways to halve the equilateral triangle

In the classroom

Remind children of some of the work they have been doing about equal sharing.

Use this language: *'What did we find out about sharing an even or odd number of objects equally?'*

Establish that the sharing of an odd number of objects resulted in 'one left over'.

Introduce the concept of 'halving' one object, e.g. one apple, or 'halving' one shape.

Ask children to visualise a whole apple and then visualise cutting it in half. Ask them to explain what they see. Reinforce the idea of sharing equally between two and this resulting in two parts of equal size.

Use the **Talking point** pictures of the circle and square. Ask children to visualise these being halved. Children could sketch the shapes and share with each other.

Show the remaining four pictures for children to compare with their own.

Pose these, or similar, questions:

* *Do any of the shapes look like the ones you saw and drew?*
* *I think that both the circles show halves. Do you agree? Why?*
* *I think that both the squares show halves. Do you agree? Why?*

Return to the square that does not show halving.

What mistake have I made? Why do you think this happened?

Re-establish the key point that halving is equal sharing between two. Agree that, although the square has two parts, they are not equal. Confirm this by folding and / or cutting each of the two shared squares along the drawn lines.

Label the halves as $\frac{1}{2}$, and use this language: *'One whole divided into two equal parts. Each part is worth* (or *called*) *a half.'*

Talking point

Which shapes show halves?

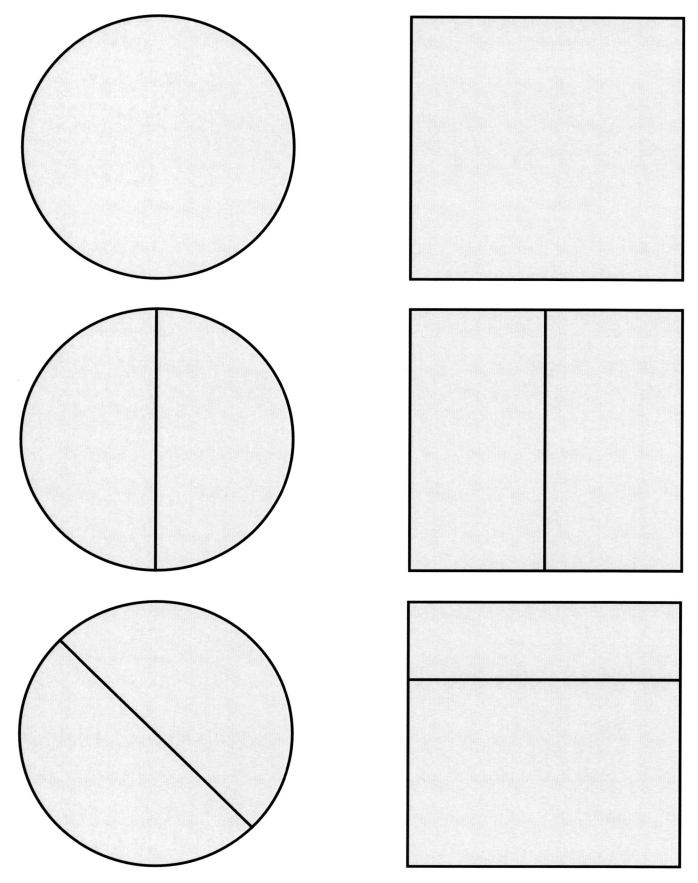

Unit 3: Finding half of a shape

Task A (Independent task)

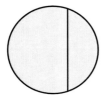 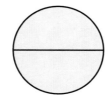 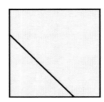 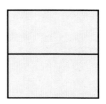

Children to each have six cut-out circles and six cut-out squares. Ask them to sort these shapes into groups of 'halves' and 'not halves'.

Use folding or cutting to confirm your decisions.

Label the halves.

> One whole divided into two equal parts. Each part is a half.

Task B (Guided learning with an adult)

Children to each have cut-out circles, squares and rectangles (at least three of each shape).

Sami made a pattern from circles, squares and rectangles.

First he cut a circle in half. Then he cut two squares into halves in different ways. He also cut two rectangles into halves in different ways.

The last shapes were each cut in two, but they were not halves.

- Use your shapes to make up the different parts of Sami's pattern.
- Label the parts that you know are a half as $\frac{1}{2}$.
- Arrange your parts in a pattern of your choice.

Task C (Independent task)

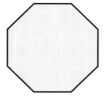  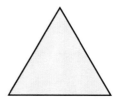 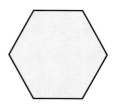

> I think I can find four different ways to halve each of these shapes.

Izzy is finding out about halves.

She has pictures of each of these shapes.

- Test each shape to find out if Izzy is correct.
- Find a way to show what you have found out.

Fluency with Fractions YEAR 1 © Rising Stars UK Ltd. 2014

UNIT 4 · Finding half linked to time

National Curriculum link:
Recognise, find and name a half as one of two equal parts of an object, shape or quantity.

[Non-statutory guidance] **Connect halves** and quarters to the equal sharing and grouping of sets of objects and **to measures.**

Year 1 pupils should already know that:
- A set of objects shared equally results in groups of an equal size
- Halving gives the same result as sharing equally between two

Supporting understanding

In Year 1, children will experience halves and then quarters in number work and then in measure.

However time is a little different: 'Tell the time to the hour and half past the hour and draw the hands on a clock face to show these times.' This extends to quarter past in Year 2, along with telling the time to 5 minutes.

Children find time more difficult as there is more than one scale, i.e. hours as 1 to 12, and minutes and seconds as 0 to 60.

> The minute hand has gone half way around the clock.
> It is half past …

Language structures will help children to talk more confidently about time and make links in learning.

Half an hour

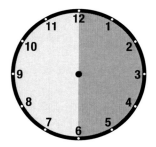 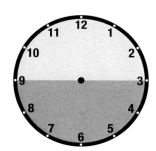

The pictures above show half an hour in two different ways. The one of the left will be used with Year 1 children to help them to recognise 'half past' the hour.

The concept of half an hour will later support children to calculate time intervals or find a time that is half an hour before or after a given time.

ANSWERS

Task A: Children's sorting of clocks in table

Task B: 1) Half past 9, half past 10, … half past 3 (if still at school)

Task C: E.g. Izzy: half past 9, half past 11 and half past 12, Tom: half past 10, half past 1 and half past 3; no, not possible (unless school starts before 8:30 a.m. or ends after 4:30 p.m.); Tom's first times must both be in the afternoon

---

In the classroom

Using the first two pictures on the **Talking point** page, revisit recognising half of a shape.

Ask children to confirm that the shapes show halves because they are 'divided into two equal parts' or 'shared equally between two'.

Now focus on the second circle and the picture of the clock. Ask children to discuss what is the same and what is different.

What do you think the shaded part shows?

What do you think I am trying to show on my clock?

Use a clock resource to show an o'clock time, e.g. 4 o'clock.

Pose these, or similar, questions for groups to think about:
- *What time does my clock show? How do you know?*
- *How long will it take before my clock shows another o'clock time?*

Language structures will help children to talk more confidently about time and make links in learning.

Model the minute hand moving all the way around to complete a whole hour.

Use this language: 'The minute hand has gone the whole way around the clock. It is **5** o'clock.'

Return to the original 'half' picture of the clock on the **Talking point** page and return the resource clock to 4 o'clock (or the time used previously). Explain that the shaded part shows how far the minute hand has moved around the clock.

How long will it take for the minute hand on the clock (resource) to move to the same place?

Use this language: 'The minute hand has gone half way around the clock. It is half past **5**.'

Talking point

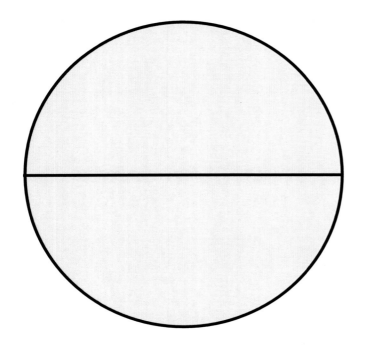

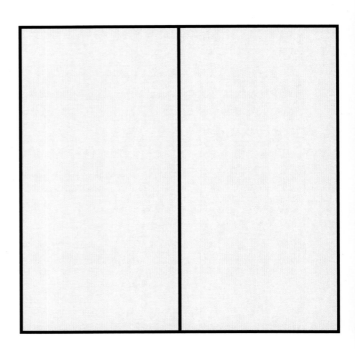

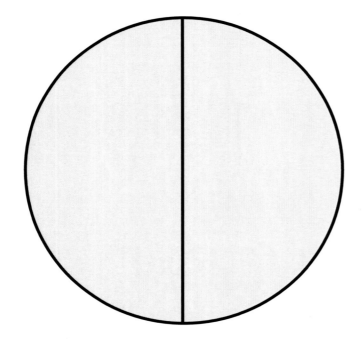

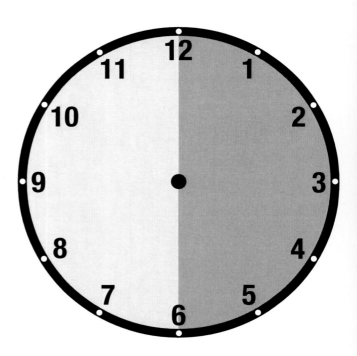

Task **A** (Independent task)

Provide children with a range of cut-out clocks showing o'clock and half-past times.

Ask children to sort the clocks onto a pre-drawn table and use the language here to describe any of the 'half-past' times that they find.

Provide children with a few blank clocks and challenge them to add a time of their own to either part of the table.

O'clock	Half past

> The minute hand has gone half way around the clock.
> It is half past ___ .

Task **B** (Independent task)

You will need a range of cut-out clocks showing o'clock and half-past times.

Class 1 are writing down all the times in the school day where the minute hand has moved half way around the clock, like the picture here.

1) Use the clocks below to show and write four different times for Class 1.

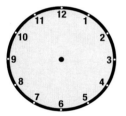 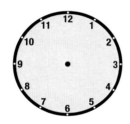 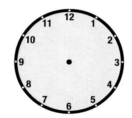 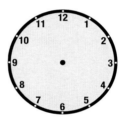

2) Use this language to prove to a friend that all your times are correct:

> The minute hand has gone half way around the clock.
> It is half past ___ .

Task **C** (Guided learning with an adult)

At the end of the school day, Izzy and Tom each write down three different times.

For each time, the minute hand has moved half way around the clock, like the picture here:

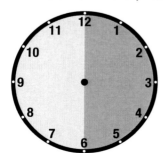

Which times in the school day did they write down?

Use the clues to help you. Is it possible to find more than one solution?

CLUES:

- Tom started by writing down two times. One is 2 hours later than the other.
- Izzy also started by writing down two times. Both these times are earlier than the first ones Tom wrote down.
- Tom also wrote down the time that his class went out to morning play.
- Izzy also wrote down the time that she had lunch.
- One of the children wrote down the time the class went home. It was later than 3 o'clock.

Finding half of a group of objects

National Curriculum link:
Recognise, find and name a half as one of two equal parts of an object, shape or quantity.

Year 1 pupils should already know that:
- A set of objects shared equally between two results in two groups of an equal size
- Halving gives the same result as sharing equally between two

Supporting understanding

In the Early Years Foundation Stage children have been solving problems involving doubling and halving. This will include practical experiences of sharing a group of objects equally between two.

> I know that I have found half because there are two equal groups. Half of **8** is **4**.

Language structures are useful to help to secure children's understanding.

These can then be used with other fractions.

Equal parts

'Equally' is a key learning point because a misconception often occurs with older children that halves relate simply to two groups, equal or otherwise.

Children should be encouraged to reason about the result of 'halving' and identify and explain examples that are not half as they are not an equal part.

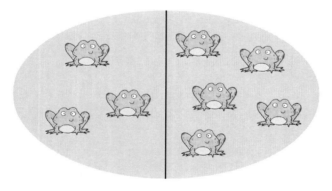

ANSWERS
Task A: Half of 10 is 5, half of 4 is 2, half of 12 is 6, half of 8 is 4, then children's own choice
Task B: Half of 14 is 7, half of 20 is 10, half of 18 is 9, half of 16 is 8, then children's own choice **Challenge:** Fred must also use what he knows about half of 4 and then add the two amounts together: 10 + 2, so half of 24 is 12
Task C: 1) Incorrect; he halved 20 but not 2, or 12 is half of 24
2) Incorrect; 8 is half of 16, or he wrote 8 because this is one of the digits in eighteen **3)** Correct **4)** Half of a group of 32 frogs is 16

In the classroom

Introduce **Talking point** Picture 1, of frogs, or something similar.

Revisit the key point that to share the frogs equally, we must make groups of an equal size.

Pose the following questions:
- *How many different ways can we share the frogs equally?*
- *How would you prove that they cannot be shared into three equal groups?*

Invite children to write, draw or show their ideas using resources such as cubes.

Use Picture 2 to probe children's understanding of equal groups. Invite children to explain what is wrong with the picture and how it can be rectified.

Model sharing equally between two groups.

They should then explain how the example should be changed so that it does represent two equal parts.

Revisit the language of 'half' and agree that sharing into two equal groups helps us to find half.

Use this language: *'I know that I have found half because there are two equal groups. Half of **8** is **4**.'*

Reinforce the language by asking different groups to consider finding half of groups of 6, 10 and 14 frogs.

Again, children can write, draw or use resources to support.

Talking point

Picture 1

Picture 2

Unit 5: Finding half of a group of objects

Task A (Independent task)

   **8**

> You choose!

Find half of each of these groups of frogs.
Show what you have found out.
Use the language in the speech bubble to help you to explain.

> I know that I have found half because there are two equal groups.
> Half of ___ is ___ .

Task B (Independent task)

> You choose!

Find half of each of these groups of frogs.
Show what you have found out.
Use the language in the speech bubble to help you to explain.

> I know that I have found half because there are two equal groups.
> Half of ___ is ___ .

Challenge:
Fred wants to find half of a group of 24 frogs. He uses what he knows about half of 20 to help him. What must he do next?

Task C (Independent task or guided learning with an adult)

Fred has been finding half of different groups of frogs.

This is what he wrote:

1) Half of a group of 22 frogs is 12.

2) Half of a group of 18 frogs is 8.

3) Half of a group of 26 frogs is 13.

4) Half of a group of ___ frogs is 16.

Check Fred's work. Is he correct?
Explain any mistakes he has made.

Now finish sentence 4 for Fred.

UNIT 6 Recognising halves in measurement

National Curriculum link:
Recognise, find and name a half as one of two equal parts of an object, shape or quantity.

Year 1 pupils should already know that:
• A set of objects shared equally between two results in two groups of an equal size
• Halving gives the same result as sharing equally between two

Supporting understanding
Within measure, Year 1 children should be taught to 'compare, describe and solve practical problems for lengths and heights [for example, long / short, longer / shorter, tall / short, double / half]'.

This provides a valuable opportunity for children to apply understanding of fractions and to see their purpose by making links to real-life situations.

I know it is half because …

I know it is not half because …

Recognising a half
Using pictures and practical experiences, children should recognise 'half' and 'double' when working with lengths and heights.

Problem solving contexts encourage children to make decisions, e.g:

Izzy is measuring straws for her model. Which straw is half the length of her ruler? How do you know?

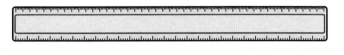

Straw 1

Straw 2

Other resources, such as integer bars, Cuisenaire rods or cubes can also be used to explore length and height.

ANSWERS
Task A: Children's practical work, showing e.g. rods of 2 and 4, or 3 and 6, etc.
Task B: 1) 10, 8, 11, 7, 9 and 12 cubes **2)** E.g. 6 and 3 cubes, 26 and 13 cubes
Task C: 1) 60, 50, 84, 56, 100 and 68 cubes **2)** E.g. 40 and 80 cubes **3)** 6

In the classroom

Use **Talking point** Picture 1 to introduce the problem that will be developed:

Izzy is measuring straws for her model.

Which piece is half the length of her ruler? How do you know? What could Izzy do to check?

Establish that the length of Straw 2 is half the length of the ruler, as we know that two straws of this length will equal the whole length of the ruler. This can be proved by making duplicate pictures of each straw and checking.

Use this language: '*I know it is half because …*' and '*I know it is not half because …*'

Label each copy of Straw 2 as $\frac{1}{2}$.

Sami has also been building a model with straws.

*Here are the different straws he has been using (show **Talking point** Picture 2), but he has now run out of Straw 2!*

What can he do? What can he use to help him?

Ask children to discuss Sami's problem and come up with a solution to test. Test their ideas using duplicate straws to prove that he can use two of Straw 4 instead.

Pose these, or similar, questions for different groups to think about:

• *Why could Sami not just use two of Straw 3?*

• *Sami needed three more of Straw 2 to finish his model. How many of Straw 4 must he use instead? How do you know?*

• *What could Sami do if he also ran out of Straw 1?*

Sami decides to check his ideas and measures his straws using cubes. Straw 1 is 12 cubes long and Straw 2 is 8 cubes long.

How long should Straw 3 and Straw 4 measure, in cubes? How do you know?

Talking point

Picture 1

Which straw is half the length of the ruler?

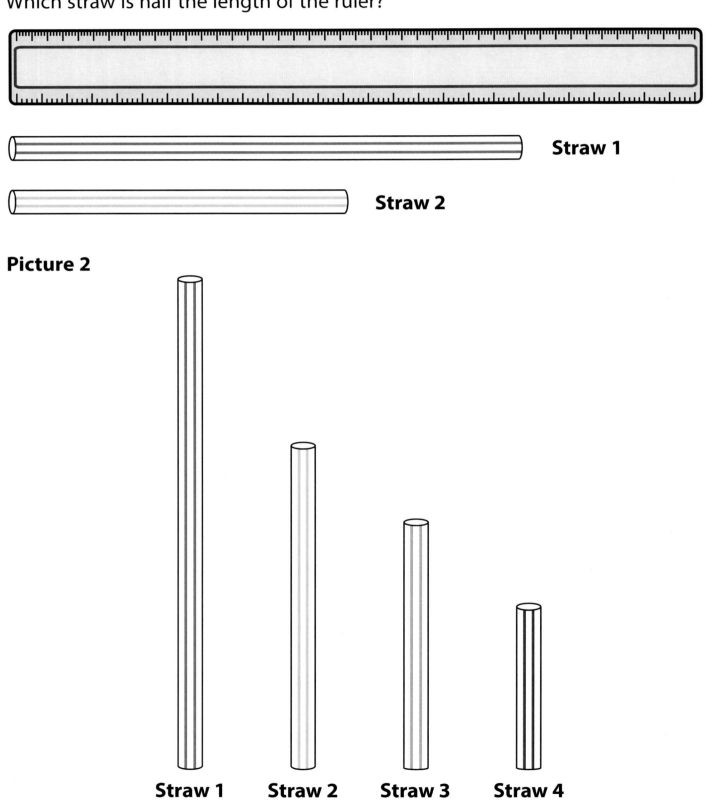

Picture 2

Task **A** (Independent task)

Sami wants to find out more about halves for another model.

- Children explore halves of lengths using integer bars, cubes or Cuisenaire rods, arranging them to show what they have found out.

Ask children to think about $\frac{1}{2}$:

- Was it easy to find a half of each of your lengths?
- Which ones were easy? Why?
- What patterns did you notice?

Task **B** (Guided learning with an adult)

Sami wants to cut some more straws for another model.

These are the lengths of the straws he will use. He uses cubes to help him to measure.

Straw 1	Straw 2	Straw 3	Straw 4	Straw 5	Straw 6	Straw 7
20 cubes	16 cubes	22 cubes	14 cubes	18 cubes	24 cubes	

Izzy measures seven more straws of her own, but when she compares each one to Sami's they all look like this!

Sami

Izzy

1) Find the length of each of Izzy's straws.

2) Make up your own lengths for Sami's Straw 7 and Izzy's Straw 7.

Task **C** (Independent task)

Abi wants to cut some pieces of ribbon for her model.

These are the lengths of the ribbons she will use. She uses cubes to help her to measure.

Ribbon 1	Ribbon 2	Ribbon 3	Ribbon 4	Ribbon 5	Ribbon 6	Ribbon 7
30 cubes	25 cubes	42 cubes	28 cubes	50 cubes	34 cubes	

Tom measures seven pieces of ribbon of his own, but when he compares each one to Abi's they all look like this!

Abi

Tom

1) Find the length of each of Tom's ribbons.

2) Make up your own lengths for Abi's Ribbon 7 and Tom's Ribbon 7.

3) Tom cuts three lots of Ribbon 2 and puts them in a line. How many of Abi's Ribbon 2 will be equal in length?

UNIT 7 Recognising less than or more than a half

National Curriculum link:

Recognise, find and name a half as one of two equal parts of an object, shape or quantity.

Year 1 pupils should already know that:

- A set of objects shared equally between two results in two groups of an equal size
- Halving gives the same result as sharing equally between two

Supporting understanding

Within measure, Year 1 children should be taught to 'compare, describe and solve practical problems for capacity and volume [for example, full / empty, more than, less than, half, half full, quarter]'.

This provides a valuable opportunity for children to apply understanding of fractions and to see their purpose by making links to real-life situations.

> I know there is less than half because …

> I know there is more than half because …

More or less than a half

Using pictures and practical experiences, children should begin to recognise 'half', 'more than a half' or 'less than a half'. Although this unit focuses on capacity, additional activities can also be related to more or less than a half turn when working with direction and movement.

Problem solving contexts encourage children to make decisions, e.g. what can Sally, Abi and Ishmal do so that they all have the same amount of water in their glasses? What fraction of a full glass of water will they each have?

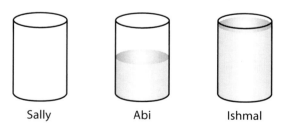

Sally   Abi   Ishmal

The problem develops so that Ishmal gives some of his water to Sally, but not as much as half. Children can then describe and show possible amounts in each glass.

ANSWERS

Task A: Children's practical work and sorting
Task B: 1) and **2)** Empty, less than half, half, more than half, full
3) Cups showing amounts of water **4)** Children's own picture showing less than half
Task C: 1) Sally empty, Abi half full, Ishmal full **2)** Practical work
3) Half each; $\frac{1}{2}$ poured from Ishmal's cup into Sally's **4)** Abi less than a half and Sally more than a half **5)** Abi, Ishmal, Sally

In the classroom

Using the pictures of the first three bottles on the **Talking point** page, ask different groups to visualise, discuss and explain where they think the level of the water will be in each. Agree a level for 'full'.

Establish that for the bottle that is half full, the same amount of the bottle is empty, as we know that each of the two parts will be equal.

Draw on the water level and label it '$\frac{1}{2}$'.

Focus on the bottle that is more than half full.

Revisit children's explanations using language such as:

I know there is more than half because …

Look at the bottom row of bottle pictures. Ask children to decide and explain if these also show more than half.

Draw on the water level for half full to confirm.

Then ask children how we can show that the last bottle does not have the same amount of water in it as the others but is also more than half full.

Pour water (you may need to colour it slightly for demonstration purposes) into a similar large bottle. Ask children to say when it is less than a half, when it stops being less than a half, when it is exactly (estimate) a half and when it becomes more than a half.

At what point is it full?

Ask children to use equipment and water or other resources to explore these ideas further.

Talking point

Look at each bottle.

Where will the water level be?

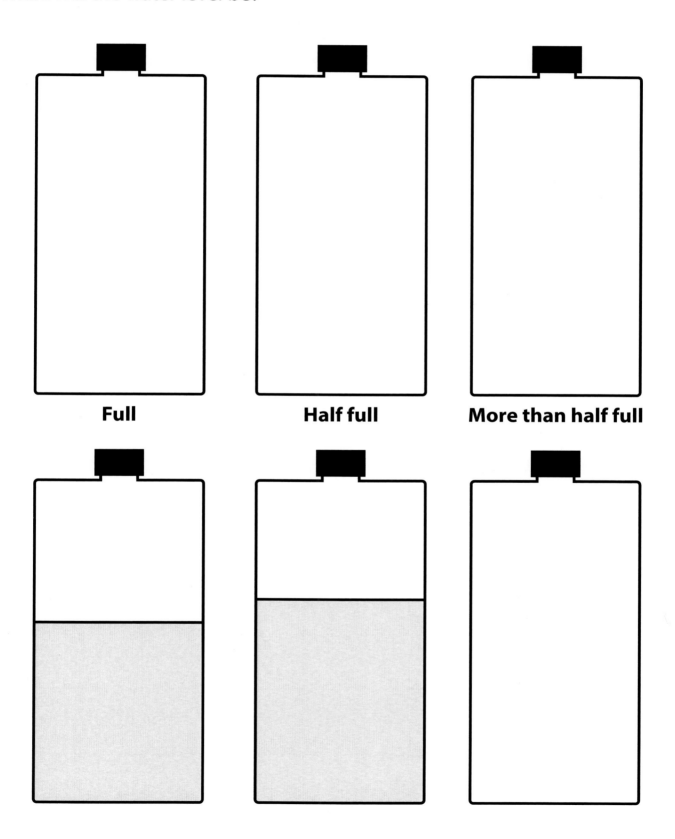

Full   **Half full**   **More than half full**

Unit 7: Recognising less than or more than a half

Task **A** (Guided learning with an adult)

You will need cards showing these pictures.

1) Find the card that shows a half. Label it.
2) Use this 'half' card to help you to sort the other cards into two groups:

Less than $\frac{1}{2}$	More than $\frac{1}{2}$

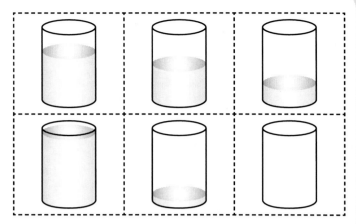

3) Using your own three cups, pour in water to match your 'half' card and one card from each of your groups.

Task **B** (Independent task)

You will need cards showing these pictures.

1) Look at the amount of water in each cup. Describe each cup using the language: *full, half full, more than half full,* etc.
2) Put the cards in order, with the least amount of water first.
3) Using your own three cups, pour in water so they look like cups on the cards showing half, less than half and more than half.
4) Use another cup to show a different amount that is less than half. Draw a picture of it.

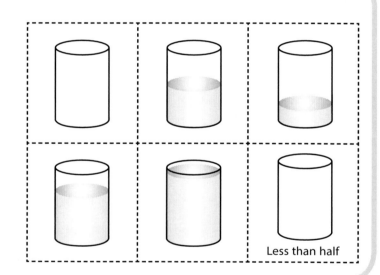

Less than half

Task **C** (Independent task)

1) Look at the amount of water in each cup. Describe each cup.
2) Use your cups and water to show how much Sally, Abi and Ishmal have.
3) Find a way to share out the water so all children have an equal amount.

   How much do they each have now?
4) Abi gives some of her water to Sally.

   Use your cups and water to show what has happened. How much do they each have now?

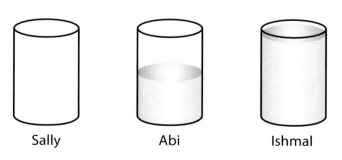

Sally   Abi   Ishmal

5) Put the cups in order, with the least amount of water first. Write the names in order.

UNIT 8 Problems about combining halves

National Curriculum link:

[Non-statutory guidance] **Recognise and combine halves** and quarters **as parts of a whole.**

Year 1 pupils should already know that:

- A set of objects shared equally between two results in two groups of an equal size
- Halving gives the same result as sharing equally between two

Supporting understanding

Through previous work, children should already know that halving gives the same result as sharing equally between two.

We can also describe this relationship in a different way: two halves are equal to a whole.

Familiar pictures and everyday contexts should be used to secure this relationship and then extended to include combining quarters in later units.

Combining halves

> There are **2** halves in a whole so **2** halves are equal to a whole.

> There are **2** halves in every **1** whole so there are **4** halves in **2** of these wholes.

As children progress to calculating with fractions in Key Stage 2, knowledge of the fractions that combine to equal a whole, e.g. two halves ($\frac{2}{2}$), four quarters ($\frac{4}{4}$), five fifths ($\frac{5}{5}$), is vital.

Although children in Year 1 will not be recording these as $\frac{2}{2}$ and $\frac{4}{4}$, it is important that they can describe the relationship and recognise that we can keep counting halves in each whole that we see.

ANSWERS
Task A: 1) 2 **2)** 4 **3)** 6 **4)** 8 **Challenge:** 3
Task B: 1) 18 **2)** E.g. there are 2 halves in 1 whole, 4 halves in 2 wholes, …, 16 halves in 8 wholes
Task C: 1) Children's workings should show that for 4 children she will need 2 oranges, 6 children need 3 oranges, etc. (we start with 2 oranges as we know that there are at least 4 children) **2)** An answer to explain that for every orange there are 2 halves so we are adding 2 for every extra orange, 15 is an odd number and will not be in the twos count

In the classroom

> Revisit the key point that halving gives the same result as sharing equally between two.
>
> Ask children to give examples of halving they have done recently inside and outside the mathematics classroom.

> Introduce **Talking point** Picture 1, perhaps as an example of halving that you have done or seen recently.
>
> *Do you think this shows halving? How do you know?*
>
> Discuss the number of halves that can be seen and then describe this. Use this language: *'There are **2** halves in a whole so **2** halves are equal to a whole.'*

> *But that was not the only orange cut in half. There were two oranges.*
>
> Ask children to discuss, sketch and compare what they think happened this time. Ask more able children to explain what would happen if there were three or four oranges.

> Using Picture 2, children should check their ideas and think about ways to use the language structure.
>
> (You may not want to use the extended sentence at this point but use a shortened version instead: *'There are four halves of oranges in two oranges.'*)

> Clarify, if necessary, that each whole has been halved so there are four halves altogether. Therefore, there are four half oranges in two whole oranges.
>
> More able children may recognise one half orange as a quarter of two whole oranges.

Talking point

Do the pictures show halving?

Picture 1

Picture 2

Task **A** (Independent task)

Peter is playing in the garden with friends.

Gran cuts some oranges for them. Each child will have half an orange.

Find out how many halves of orange Gran has when she cuts:

1) 1 orange   **2)** 2 oranges

3) 3 oranges   **4)** 4 oranges

> There are ___ halves of orange in ___ oranges.

Challenge:

Gran has 6 halves of orange. How many oranges did she cut?

Task **B** (Independent task or guided learning with an adult)

Izzy is playing in the garden with friends.

Gran cuts some oranges for them. Each child will have half an orange.

> Mmm, I only have **9** oranges. How many children can have half an orange each?

1) Help Gran with her problem.
   Write down what you find out.

2) Gran does **not** cut all of the oranges.
   How many different numbers of halves of orange can she cut?
   Use the table below to help you.

> There are ___ halves of orange in ___ oranges.

Oranges	1	2						
Halves	2							

Task **C** (Independent task)

Jade and Ishmal are playing in the garden with friends.

Gran cuts some oranges for them. Each child will have half an orange.

> Mmm, I can count an even number of children.
> I wonder how many oranges I need?

1) Help Gran with her problem.
   Write down what you find out.

2) Gran cuts the oranges. She counts 15 halves.
   How will you explain to Gran that she has made a mistake?

UNIT 9 Equal sharing between four

National Curriculum link:

[Non-statutory guidance] **Connect** halves and **quarters to the equal sharing and grouping of sets of objects** and to measures.

Year 1 pupils should already know that:

- A set of objects shared equally between two results in two groups of an equal size
- Halving gives the same result as sharing equally between two

Supporting understanding

The work that we have been doing about halving builds on the principle of sharing equally. It is just as important for children to appreciate 'unequal sharing' so that they recognise when they have made errors in their fraction work.

Continue to use activities, pictures and apparatus to encourage children to recognise and talk about equal sharing, using language to support.

> I know … is shared equally because …

> I know … is not shared equally because …

This unit will explore sharing equally between four.

Equal sharing

We know that early experience of sharing, in the classroom and in real life, is likely to be through the idea of 'one for you, one for you, one for you and one for me, …'. This supports understanding of finding a quarter by sharing equally between four.

Questions to ask could include: *'Is it easier for four children to share the pencils or the pens equally between them? Why?'*

ANSWERS

Task A: Pennies in boxes 1 and 4 share equally **Challenge:** E.g. 4 and get 1 each, 16 and get 4 each

Task B: Children's own recordings to show that alternate even numbers (i.e. multiples of 4) can be shared equally

Task C: 1) As for B, but perhaps more systematic **2)** E.g. 'Starting from 4, count 4 pennies each time', 'Not all the even numbers work, you miss one out and then the next one works' or something referring to counting in fours **3)** E.g. 'Yes, because 8 shares equally between 4 and 80 is 10 times bigger'

In the classroom

Use the **Talking point** to introduce the problem:

Tom, Sally, Izzy and Ishmal want to share their group's pens and pencils equally between the four of them.

Ask children to discuss and give an example of when they have shared things equally.

Establish the key point that when a group of objects is 'shared equally' it results in groups of an equal size.

Using the pictures of pens and pencils provided on the **Talking point** page, pose the following questions for different groups to think about:

- *How many pencils will each child have? How do you know?*
- *Why is it easier to share the pencils than the pens?*
- *How many more pens do they need so they can share them equally? Do you think there could be more than one answer?*

(Look for children who recognise that three more, seven more, etc. would also work.)

I know … is shared equally because …

Children could check by sharing pens and pencils between four children; that they get a 'quarter' of the pens each can also be introduced.

What do we notice about the number that could be shared equally and the one that could not?

Refer to previous work about odd and even numbers and halving. Children will find out later that not all even numbers can be shared equally between four with none left over.

Look at the next set of **Talking point** pictures.

When Tom got home he wanted to find out more about sharing equally between four. He decided to use the coins in his money box.

He was excited to find out that his pennies could also be shared equally between four.

Which group of pennies belonged to Tom? How do you know? What can you show me? How many pennies would children get each?

Which group did not belong to Tom? How do you know?

Ask children to explore independently other numbers of pennies that share equally between four.

Talking point

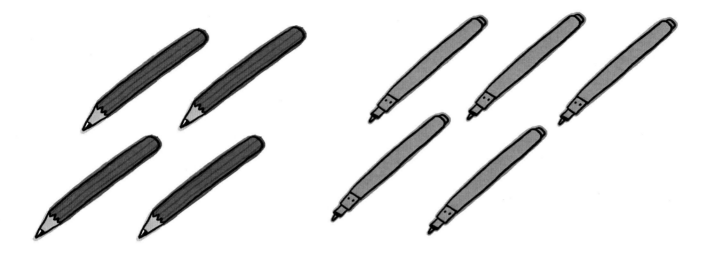

Which group of coins can be shared equally between four?

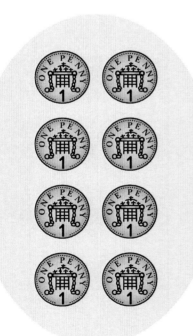

Unit 9: Equal sharing between four

Task A (Indpendent task)

Tom thinks about different numbers of pennies in a money box.
Which ones share equally between four?

1) 2) 3) 4)

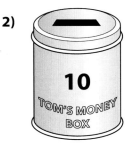 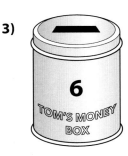 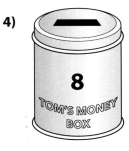

Show what you have found out.

Challenge:

Can you find a different number of pennies that Tom can share equally between four children?
How many pennies will they have each?

Task B (Guided learning with an adult)

I know that all even numbers can be shared equally between **2** so I think that an even number of pennies can all be shared equally between **4**.

What do you think?
Investigate Tom's idea and show what you have found out.

Task C (Independent task)

I know that all even numbers can be shared equally between **2** so I think that an even number of pennies can all be shared equally between **4**.

What do you think?

1) Investigate Tom's idea and be prepared to show what you have found out.
2) What will you tell Tom to help him to find other numbers of pennies that can be shared equally between four?
3) Do you think that 80 pennies can be shared equally between four? Why?

UNIT 10 Finding quarter of a shape

National Curriculum link:

Recognise, find and name a quarter as one of four equal parts of an object, shape or quantity.

Year 1 pupils should already know that:

- A set of objects shared equally between four results in four groups of an equal size
- Finding a quarter gives the same result as sharing equally between four

Supporting understanding

Children have been exploring equal sharing and have identified the numbers that can be shared easily, i.e. even numbers. They recognise that when odd numbers are shared between two, there is one left over.

This unit develops the idea of equal sharing to quarters and supports children in recognising quarters in shape.

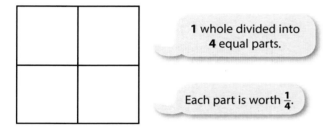

1 whole divided into **4** equal parts.

Each part is worth $\frac{1}{4}$.

Finding quarters

Find and share pictures that show an object or a group of objects shared equally, e.g:

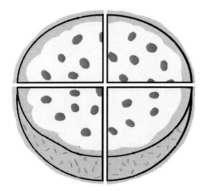

Encourage children to discuss what they notice. This may well include the phrases 'shared between four', 'split into four pieces', 'cut in four'.

Make sure to establish the 'equal sharing' and the 'equal parts' that result.

ANSWERS

Task A: Children's own designs

Task B: Yes, it is possible, the octagon being the most challenging

Task C: 1) Circle **2)** Hexagon **3)** Rectangle **4)** Octagon **5)** A quarter of a child's chosen shape; each part is worth $\frac{1}{4}$

In the classroom

Remind children of some of the work they have been doing about finding a half and equal sharing:

How do we know that we have found a half of an object or a shape? What do we need to remember?

Reinforce that halving is the same as equal sharing between two and the result is two equal parts.

But what happens when we want to cut an object or shape into four equal parts? What can we use to help us?

Use the **Talking point** to introduce the concept of finding a quarter of one object, e.g. one apple, or one shape.

Ask children to visualise a whole apple and then visualise sharing it equally between four.

Children could sketch, share with each other and check the number of equal parts that they now have. Ask them to explain what they see.

Reinforce the idea of equal parts. Draw lines on the first two pictures on the **Talking point** page to create four equal parts.

Show the remaining four pictures for children to compare with their own.

Pose these, or similar, questions:

- *Do any of the shapes look like the ones you saw and drew?*
- *I think that both the circles show quarters. Do you agree? Why?*
- *I think that both the squares show quarters. Do you agree? Why?*

Return to the square that does not show quarters:

What mistake have I made? Why do you think this happened?

Re-establish the key point that finding a quarter is equal sharing between four. Although the square has four parts, they are not equal. Confirm this by folding and / or cutting each of the squares along the drawn lines.

On the square shared equally, label each quarter as $\frac{1}{4}$.

Use this language: *'One whole divided into four equal parts. Each part is worth* (or *called*) *a quarter.'*

Talking point

Can you find a quarter of these shapes?

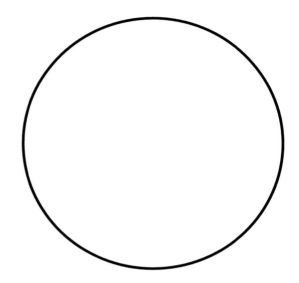

Do any of these shapes look like the ones you saw and drew?

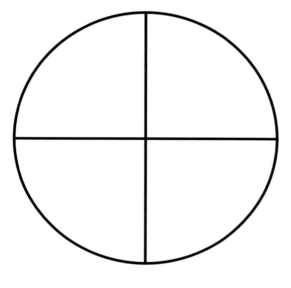
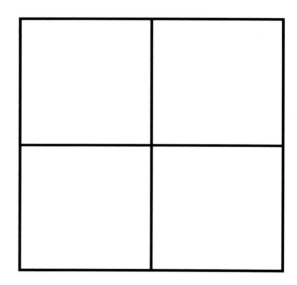

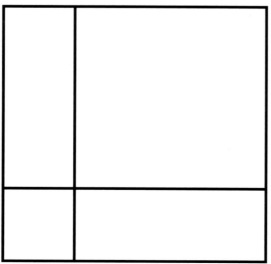
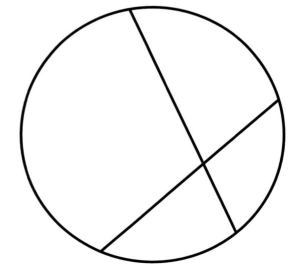

Task **A** (Guided learning with an adult)

You will need of cut-out circles, squares and rectangles (at least two of each).

Sami made a pattern from circles, squares and rectangles.

First he cut a circle into quarters. Then he cut two squares into quarters in different ways. He also cut two rectangles into quarters in different ways.

The last shapes were each cut into four, but they were not quarters.

- Use your shapes to make up the different parts of Sami's pattern.
- Label the parts that you know are a quarter as $\frac{1}{4}$.
- Arrange your parts in a pattern of your choice.

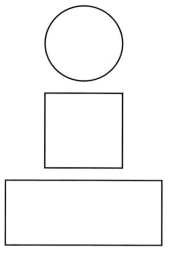

Task **B** (Independent task)

Sally is finding out about quarters.
She has pictures of each of these shapes.

I think I can find two different ways to find quarters of each of these shapes.

What do you think?
Find a way to show what you have found out.

Task **C** (Independent task or guided learning with an adult)

Provide children with a set of paper shapes, to include a circle, hexagon, rectangle and octagon (so that their quarters will match the images below).

Ishmal has been cutting shapes into quarters. These are quarters from each of his shapes.

1)   2)   3)   4)

Use what you know about quarters to find the whole shape each time.
Draw the whole shape and label the quarters.

HINT: You can fold paper shapes to help you.

5) Draw around a different shape. Find and cut out a quarter for your teacher to guess.

Relating quarters to halves

National Curriculum link:

Recognise, find and name a half as one of two equal parts of an object, shape or quantity.

Recognise, find and name a quarter as one of four equal parts of an object, shape or quantity.

Year 1 pupils should already know that:

- A set of objects shared equally between two results in two groups of an equal size
- A set of objects shared equally between four results in four groups of an equal size
- Finding a quarter gives the same result as sharing equally between four

Supporting understanding

Children have been using equal sharing to help find a half or quarter of a shape or object. They should continue to visualise and explain what happens as a result of halving and quartering.

This unit develops these ideas but also introduces the concept of halving and halving again.

> **One** whole divided into **four** equal parts. Each part is worth $\frac{1}{4}$.

> **One** whole divided into **two** equal parts and then each part is divided equally into **two** again. Each part is now worth $\frac{1}{4}$.

Relating quarters to halves

Find and share pictures that show an object shared equally between two and then four.

Encourage children to discuss what they notice.

Key knowledge when working with division and fractions is that we can find a quarter by halving and halving again.

Each half is divided in two again to result in four equal pieces.

Other activities to relate quarters to halves will include making two quarter turns to equal one half turn.

ANSWERS
Task A: 1) $\frac{1}{2}$ of 8 is 4 so $\frac{1}{4}$ of 8 is 2 **2)** $\frac{1}{2}$ of 12 is 6 so $\frac{1}{4}$ of 12 is 3
3) $\frac{1}{2}$ of 20 is 10 so $\frac{1}{4}$ of 20 is 5 **4)** $\frac{1}{2}$ of 16 is 8 so $\frac{1}{4}$ of 16 is 4
Task B: 1) $\frac{1}{2}$ of 20 is 10 so $\frac{1}{4}$ of 20 is 5 **2)** $\frac{1}{2}$ of 16 is 8 so $\frac{1}{4}$ of 16 is 4
3) $\frac{1}{2}$ of 40 is 20 so $\frac{1}{4}$ of 40 is 10 **4)** $\frac{1}{2}$ of 24 is 12 so $\frac{1}{4}$ of 24 is 6 **5)** 12
Task C:

Whole	12	16	28	100	80
Half	6	8	14	50	40
Quarter	3	4	7	25	20

In the classroom

> Remind children about some of the work they have been doing to find quarters of a shape or object.
>
> Ask children to discuss what they know about quarters and how they differ from halves.

> Ask children to visualise a whole orange and then visualise cutting it in half.
>
> Use the **Talking point** Picture 1 or a real orange to confirm what happens.
>
> *But what happens when each of the halves is cut in half again?*
>
> Ask children to visualise and then share with each other to check the number of equal parts we have now.
>
> Use Picture 2 to confirm.

> Establish that finding quarters is the same as finding halves and then halving again.
>
> Suggest that this may be able help us to find a quarter of a group of 8 objects or 12 objects.
>
> Ask children to discuss the suggestion using resources, such as cubes, to help them.

> Using children's ideas, model finding a quarter of 8 by sharing into two parts and then sharing each part into two parts again.

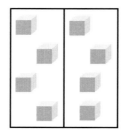 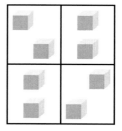

Repeat with 12 if necessary. Children will develop this idea further in independent tasks.

Talking point

Picture 1

What happens when you cut an orange in half?

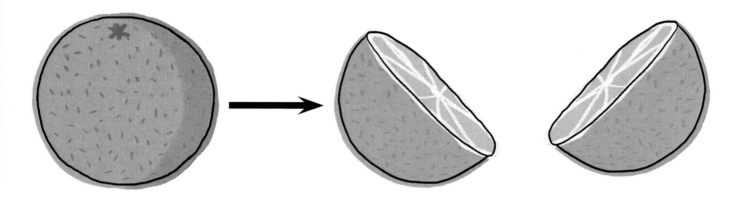

Picture 2

What happens when you cut the halves in half again?

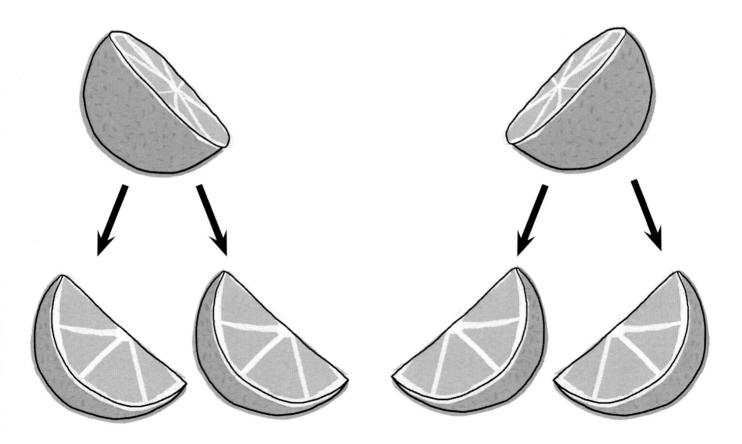

Task **A** (Independent task or guided learning with an adult)

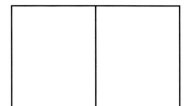 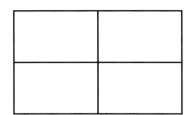

Use the shapes to help you to find halves and quarters of each amount.
Write about each, using the language in the speech bubble.

$\frac{1}{2}$ of 4 is 2 so $\frac{1}{4}$ of 4 is 1

1) 8 cubes   **2)** 12 cubes   **3)** 20 cubes   **4)** 16 cubes

Task **B** (Independent task)

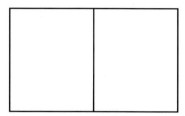 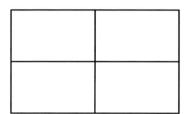

Use the shapes to help you to find halves and quarters of each amount.
Write about each, using the language in the speech bubble.

$\frac{1}{2}$ of 8 is 4 so $\frac{1}{4}$ of 8 is 2

1) 20   **2)** 16   **3)** 40   **4)** 24

5) Sami wrote $\frac{1}{2}$ of ___ is 6 so $\frac{1}{4}$ of ___ is 3.

What is the missing number?

Task **C** (Independent task)

Sami used this table to record what he found out about halves and quarters.

Whole			28		
Half	6			50	
Quarter		4			20

Fill in Sami's missing information.

UNIT 12 Finding quarter of a group of objects

National Curriculum link:
Recognise, find and name a quarter as one of four equal parts of an object, shape or quantity.

Year 1 pupils should already know that:
- A set of objects shared equally between four results in four groups of an equal size
- Finding a quarter gives the same result as sharing equally between four

Supporting understanding

Children should have plenty of practical experience of finding half of a shape, object or group of objects.

In Unit 11, they looked in more depth at the relationship between halves and quarters.

This will support them in Year 3 with eighths.

Language structures to emphasise 'equal sharing' (as used with halves) should be used here. This can then be used with other fractions, including thirds in Year 2.

> I know that I have found quarters because there are **four** equal groups. A quarter of **12** is **3**.

Finding a quarter

Children should be encouraged to reason about the result of 'finding a quarter' and identify and explain examples that are not quarters as there are not four equal parts.

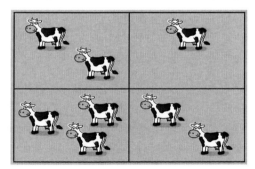

They should then explain how the example should be changed so that it does represent four equal parts.

Using halving and halving again will provide an alternative strategy to sharing equally between four.

ANSWERS
Task A: A) 2 **B)** 3 **C)** 5 **D)** 4
Task B: 1) Incorrect: quarter of 12 is 3 **2)** Correct **3)** Correct
4) Quarter of 8 is 2 **5)** E.g. a quarter of 40 is 10
Task C: 1) Half of 16 is 8 and half of 8 is 4, quarter of 16 is 4; half of 20 is 10 and half of 10 is 5, quarter of 20 is 5, etc. **2)** A quarter of 20 is 5; 28 is 8 more than 20 so he just needs to add a quarter of 8; 32 is 12 more than 20 so he just needs to add a quarter of 12

In the classroom

> Introduce **Talking point** Picture 1, showing the cows in Farmer Green's field.
>
> Ask children to discuss and explain what they think the picture is showing.

> Pose the problem that Farmer Brown also wants to arrange his cows equally in four areas, but he has 12 cows altogether:
>
> *What should he do?*
>
> Invite children to write, draw or show their ideas using resources such as cubes.
>
> Encourage more able children to explain why Farmer Brown knows immediately that there will not be six cows in each area.

> Look at Picture 2:
>
> *This is Farmer Brown's first go at arranging his cows. What do you think? What mistake has he made?*
>
> Ask children to feed back and then confirm by modelling that there are three cows in each section.

> Show that the same result can be reached by halving 12 and then halving again.
>
> Label each section of the field as $\frac{1}{4}$. Ask children to count the quarters to agree that there are four equal parts.

> *The next day, Farmer Brown needs to milk a quarter of his cows before breakfast.*
>
> *How can you explain to Farmer Brown that he needs to milk more than two cows before breakfast?*

> Use this language: '*I know that I have found quarters because there are four equal groups. A quarter of … is …*'

Talking point

Picture 1

What is the picture showing?

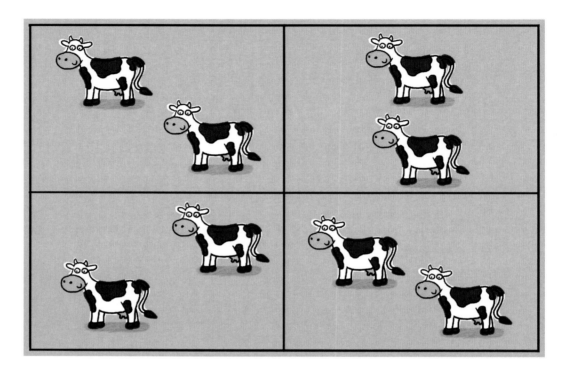

Picture 2

Task A (Independent task)

Farmer Brown decides to arrange his chickens in the same way.

$\frac{1}{4}$	$\frac{1}{4}$
$\frac{1}{4}$	$\frac{1}{4}$

A)  8

B)  12

C)  20

D)  16

Find quarter of each of these groups of chickens.
Show what you have found out.
Use the speech bubbles to help you to explain.

> I know that I have found quarters because I have **four** equal groups.

> A quarter of _____ is _____.

Task B (Guided learning with an adult)

Farmer Brown has been finding a quarter of different groups of chickens.

This is what he wrote:

1) A quarter of a group of 12 chickens is 4.

2) A quarter of a group of 20 chickens is 5.

3) A quarter of a group of 16 chickens is 4.

4) A quarter of a group of ___ chickens is 2.

5) A quarter of a group of ___ chickens is ___ .

Check Farmer Brown's work for sentences 1, 2 and 3. Is he correct? Explain any mistakes he has made.
Now finish sentence 4 for Farmer Brown.
Make up your own example for sentence 5.

Task C (Independent task)

Farmer Brown has been finding a quarter of different groups of chickens.

A)  16

B) 20

C)  40

D)  80

1) Prove to Farmer Brown that he can find a quarter of his group of chickens each time by finding half and then half again.

2) Prove to Farmer Brown that he can use what he knows about finding a quarter of a group of 20 chickens to help him to find a quarter of a group of 28 chickens and then 32 chickens.

UNIT 13 Recognising quarters in measurement

National Curriculum link:
Recognise, find and name a quarter as one of four equal parts of an object, shape or quantity.

Year 1 pupils should already know that:
- A set of objects shared equally results in groups of an equal size
- Finding a quarter gives the same result as sharing equally between four

Supporting understanding

Within measure, Year 1 children should be taught to 'compare, describe and solve practical problems for capacity and volume [for example, full / empty, more than, less than, half, half full, quarter].'

Earlier units provided experiences for children to apply understanding of fractions to practical contexts and make links to real-life situations.

> I know it is quarter because I can see **four** equal parts.

> I know it is not quarter because …

Recognising quarters

Using pictures and practical experiences, children should recognise quarters when working with capacity and volume.

Problem solving contexts encourage children to make decisions, e.g. *Peter and Abi are making orange squash for a party*:

In this example, children will need to look carefully as not all glasses are the same size. They should learn that they must compare the fraction to the whole.

ANSWERS
Task A: Children's sorting and labelling
Task B: Children's sorting and recording **Challenge:** 2
Task C: 1) 3 **2)** 9 **3)** 4 **4)** 2

In the classroom

Using **Talking point** Picture 1, introduce the problem that will be developed:

Peter and Abi are making orange squash for a party.

Abi filled glasses $\frac{1}{4}$ full. Peter did not.

Ask children to discuss and explain which glasses of squash Abi made. Ask more able children to estimate the fraction of squash Peter made.

Discuss what has made this task a little more difficult, i.e. not all the glasses are the same size.

Establish that we must look at the fraction compared to the whole to decide if it is quarter or not.

Use this language: '*I know it is quarter because I can see four equal parts*' and '*I know it is not quarter because …*'

Look for children who refer to four equal parts.

Ask more able children to feed back on some of the fractions they estimated and explain their thinking.

Use Picture 2 to think about Peter's orange squash.

Pose these, or similar, questions for different groups to think about:

- *Which glass would you most like to have? Why?*
- *Compare each of these fractions to $\frac{1}{4}$. How can you explain which are more or less than quarter?*
- *Peter puts another $\frac{1}{4}$ of a glass of squash into each of the glasses. What can you tell me about the fraction in each glass now?*

Explore children's ideas using language structures and modelling to help explain.

Use a practical model with liquid to show that a further $\frac{1}{4}$ added to the middle glass in Picture 2 results in a full glass.

Talking point

Picture 1

Which glasses are $\frac{1}{4}$ full?

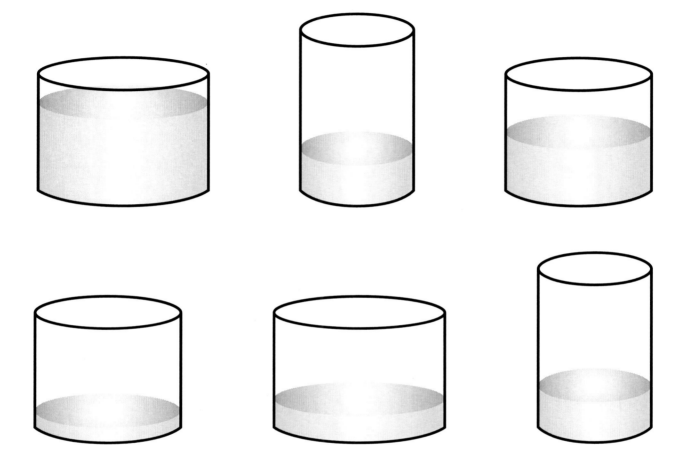

Picture 2

Which glass would you choose?

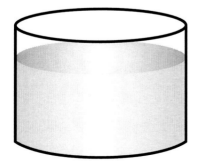 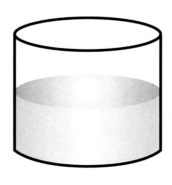 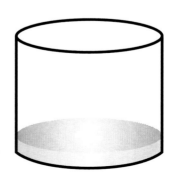

Unit 13: Recognising quarters in measurement

Task A (Independent task or guided learning with an adult)

Ask children to sort a range of pictures of different containers into 'quarters' and 'not quarters', e.g:

Ask children record their findings in their own way and label the pictures using 'more than' and 'less than'.

Challenge:
Abi makes another glass of squash. It is also $\frac{1}{4}$ full. Draw her glass and put it in the right place in your work.

Task B (Independent task)

1) Sort the containers into groups to show 'quarters' and 'not quarters'.
2) Look at the 'not quarters' group and decide if each one is more or less than $\frac{1}{4}$. Write down your ideas.
3) Draw a container of your own to add to each group.

Challenge:
Abi thinks that 8 egg cups of squash will fill this glass. How many egg cups of squash will she need to fill $\frac{1}{4}$ of the glass?

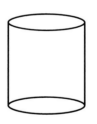

Task C (Independent task or guided learning with an adult)

Abi and Peter are using different glasses for lemon squash.
Abi can fill each of her glasses using 12 egg cups of lemon squash.
1) How many egg cups of lemon squash will she need to fill $\frac{1}{4}$ of a glass?
2) How many egg cups of lemon squash will she need so that only $\frac{1}{4}$ of her glass is empty?

Peter can fill each of his glasses using 20 egg cups of lemon squash.
3) He uses 20 egg cups of squash altogether to fill $\frac{1}{4}$ of each of his glasses.
   How many glasses of lemon squash did he make?
4) What if he makes each glass $\frac{1}{2}$ full? How many glasses of lemon squash can he make now?

UNIT 14 Finding and combining quarters of objects

National Curriculum link:
[Non-statutory guidance] **Recognise and combine halves and quarters as parts of a whole.**
Recognise, find and name a quarter as one of four equal parts of an object, shape or quantity.

Year 1 pupils should already know that:
- Two halves combine to equal a whole
- Finding a quarter gives the same result as sharing equally between four

Supporting understanding

In Year 2, children will be counting in fraction steps of halves and quarters. They will need to apply knowledge of combining halves to equal a whole and quarters to equal a whole. They will also need to recognise that two quarters are equal to a half.

Everyday pictures can be used to help children to recognise some of these relationships.

Combining quarters

> There are **four** quarters in a whole so **four** quarters are equal to a whole.

> There are **eight** quarters in **two** wholes.

As children progress to calculating with fractions in Key Stage 2, knowledge of the fractions that combine to equal a whole, e.g. two halves $\left(\frac{2}{2}\right)$, four quarters $\left(\frac{4}{4}\right)$, five fifths $\left(\frac{5}{5}\right)$, is vital.

Although children in Year 1 will not be recording these as $\frac{2}{2}$ and $\frac{4}{4}$, it is important that they can describe the relationship and recognise that we can keep counting quarters in each whole that we see.

Also, children can combine quarter turns to show half, three-quarter and full turns.

ANSWERS
Task A: 1) 4 **2)** 8 **Challenge:** 2
Task B: 1) 20 quarters **2)** E.g. there are 4 quarters in 1 whole, 8 quarters in 2 wholes, 16 quarters in 4 wholes
Task C: 1) Children's workings should show that for 3 bowls Stan needs 2 apples, for 5 bowls he needs 3 apples, etc. (since we know he counts 'bowls', it is likely there is more than 1 bowl **2)** 5 **3)** 9 **4)** Two quarters or one half left over

In the classroom

Revisit the key point that finding quarters gives the same result as sharing equally between four.

Ask children to give examples of sharing equally between four they have come across recently (inside and outside the mathematics classroom).

Share the context of cutting an apple so it can be shared equally between four, perhaps as an example of something you have done or seen recently.

Ask children to discuss, sketch and compare what they think happened when the apple was cut. More able children should also think about a way to cut the apple into quarters, e.g. half and half again.

Using **Talking point** Picture 1, ask children to compare their ideas and explain what is different:

What mistake have I made? What should I have done?

Use the concept of halving and halving again to cut an apple into quarters.

Count the number of quarters that can be seen ('*One quarter, two quarters, …*') and then describe them.

Use this language: '*There are four quarters in a whole so four quarters are equal to a whole.*'

Use Picture 2 to pose the problem that there are not one but two apples to cut into quarters.

Ask children to discuss what they think happens this time. Ask more able children to explain what would happen if there were three apples.

Confirm, and model if necessary, that each whole is cut into quarters so there are eight quarters altogether.

Use this language: '*There are eight quarters in two wholes.*'

Talking point

Picture 1

Are these quarters?

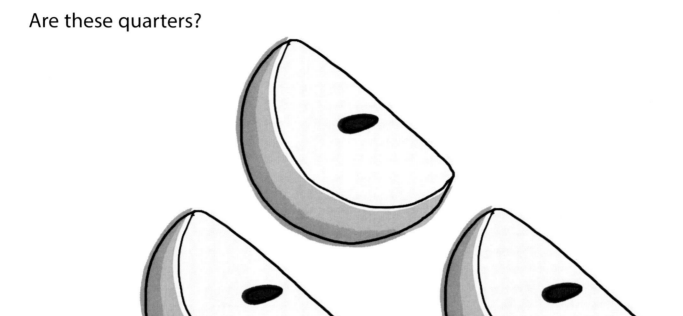

Picture 2

What happens when I cut each of these apples in quarters?
How many quarters will I have?

Task **A** (Independent task or guided learning with an adult)

Stan is cutting apples to put in fruit salads. He cuts each apple into quarters.
Give children pre-prepared modelling clay balls to represent the apples.
Ask them to find out how many quarters Stan will have when he cuts:

1)   **2)**

Encourage children to count the quarters each time.

Challenge:

Stan has 8 quarters of apple. How many apples did he cut?

Task **B** (Independent task or guided learning with an adult)

Stan is cutting apples to put in fruit salads.
He cuts each apple into quarters.

Mmm, I only have **5** apples.
How many quarters can I cut?

1) Help Stan with his problem.
Write down what you find out.

2) Stan does not cut all of the apples.
How many different numbers of quarters can
he cut and how many apples does he use
each time?

There are ___ quarters in ___ wholes.

Task **C** (Independent task)

Stan is cutting apples to put in fruit salads.
He cuts each apple into quarters. He will put
2 quarters into each fruit salad bowl.

Mmm, I can count an odd number
of fruit salad bowls. I wonder how
many apples I need?

HINT: Remember that there
is an odd number of bowls.

1) Help Stan with his problem.
Write down what you find out.

2) Stan cuts the apples. He counts 20 quarters.
How many apples did he use?

3) How many fruit salads does he make?

4) What fraction of an apple is left over?

UNIT 15 Problems about fractions

National Curriculum link:

Recognise, find and name a half as one of two equal parts of an object, shape or quantity.

Recognise, find and name a quarter as one of four equal parts of an object, shape or quantity.

Year 1 pupils should already know that:

- We use fractions to describe parts of a whole
- We can use equal sharing to help us make sense of fractions
- We can count the number of fractions in a whole

Supporting understanding

Throughout the units, children develop an understanding of halves and quarters and make links to real-life contexts.

Developing the use of pictures can help children to recognise relationships between some of the fractions they are using and prepare them for working with equivalent fractions from Year 2.

In this unit, children will look at turns and link these to their work on fractions. They will use knowledge that there are two quarter turns in half a turn, etc. and extend this to thinking about three quarters of a turn.

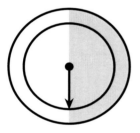
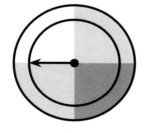

Abi   Tom

Solving problems

It is important that children have plenty of opportunities to apply knowledge and skills. This not only secures understanding but also provides evidence of learning.

To be successful, children must first make sense of the problem and find a starting point. Encourage children to tell the story of the problem, role-play it or sketch something that helps them to make sense of it.

As teachers, we need to model how to be a problem solver and show children how to find starting points.

ANSWERS
Task A: 1) 4 **2)** 8
Task B: 1) 2 **2)** 8 **3)** $\frac{1}{4}$ because 5 is $\frac{1}{4}$ of 20
Task C: 1) 150 **2)** 225 **3)** One full container and another three quarters full **4)** 5 quarters

In the classroom

> Tom and Abi are enjoying the different activities at the local fair.
>
> *They start with the 'Spinning Wheel' game.*
>
> Using **Talking point** Picture 1, pose these questions:
> - *Who made the biggest turn with the wheel? How do you know?*
> - *What fraction can be used to describe the turn that Abi made with the wheel?*
> - *And Tom? What fraction describes his turn of the wheel?*

> Show Picture 2:
> *A full turn will score 40 points.*
> *How can we use this information to find out how many points Tom and Abi scored on their second go?*
> Share ideas and ways to share 40 equally between two and then between four.

> *On their last go, Abi scored 10 points more than Tom.*
> Pose these, or similar, questions for different groups to think about:
> - *What fraction of a turn would Abi have made to score 20 points?*
> - *What fraction of a turn can they each have made so Abi scores 10 points more than Tom? Is there more than one possibility?*

> Use Picture 3 to introduce the next activity that Tom, Abi and their friends play:
>
> *In the Water Race, runners use buckets of water to try to fill up as many containers as they can.*
>
> *Abi has put one full bucket into the container.*
> - *What fraction of the container is full so far?*
> - *How many quarters are needed to fill one container? How many buckets is this?*
> Discuss and model ideas. Children will find out more about the race in their tasks.

Talking point

Who made the biggest turn with the wheel? How do you know?

Picture 1   Turn 1

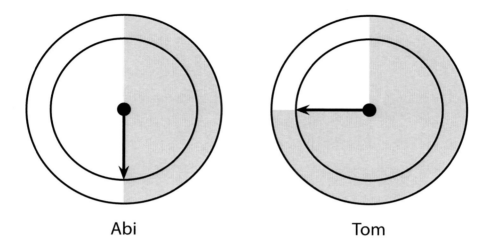

Abi   Tom

Picture 2   Turn 2

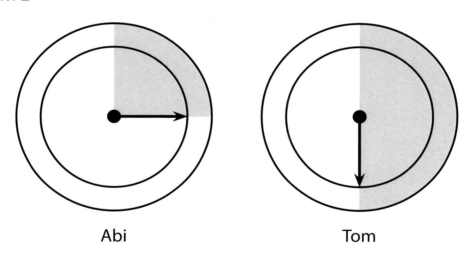

Abi   Tom

Picture 3   The Water Race

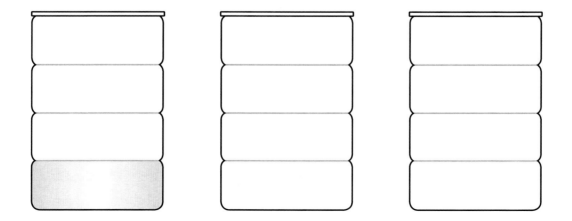

Task **A** (Guided learning with an adult)

Work together on a practical task to model the events of the Water Race considered in the main lesson.
Start with three identical empty containers. Estimate and represent the water shown in the first container in Picture 3 on the **Talking point** page, and then add the water in quarters, counting as you go.
(You can also do this using Picture 3, covering quarters with counters as you go.)
Ask children to describe and write the fraction each time.
Then ask what fraction still needs to be collected to fill the container.

1) How many quarters are needed to fill 1 container?

2) How many quarters are needed to fill 2 containers?

Task **B** (Independent task)

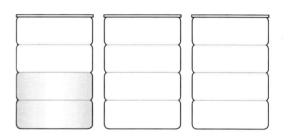

At the end of the race we only had 2 full containers, but what fraction of the last container did we fill?

1) How many more quarters did Abi's team need to fill 1 container?

2) How many quarters altogether did they need to fill 2 containers?

3) Abi's teacher used 20 bottles of water to fill a container.
There is only enough water in the last container to fill 5 bottles.
What fraction of the last container did the team fill? How do you know?

Task **C** (Independent task)

Teams score 100 points for every full container, but they can also use what they know about fractions to help to work out scores for other amounts of water.
Find the number of points that teams would score for these containers:

1)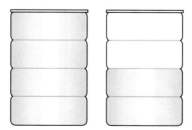

2)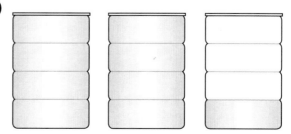

3) Draw or describe the water collected by the team who scored 175 points.

4) How many more quarters does this team need to fill three containers?